INVISIBLE BORDERS

new women's writing from Cornwall

Edited by
Linda Cleary

Hypatia Publications

First published September 2020 by Hypatia Publications

Rights for all poems belong to the authors

For copyright of poems used with permission from the publishers Bloodaxe, Seren and Offord Road Books see Acknowledgements p82.

ISBN (paperback): 978-1-872229-67-6
ISBN (eBook): 978-1-872229-68-3

Layout and typeset in Palatino in-house
by Linda Cleary at Hypatia Publications

Printed in Great Britain at Headland Printers, Cornwall on FSC accredited paper stocks. Chemical free digital printing process, from an environmentally friendly run factory.

The publication of this book was funded by Cultivator Cornwall. See Acknowledgements p82.

Hypatia Publications
imprint of
The Hypatia Trust
Penzance Cornwall
www.hypatia-trust.org.uk

CONTENTS

For you and for all that take a step..

INTRODUCTION

This first publication from a new Cornish press, celebrating women's writing connected to this elemental region, takes you on a journey through Cornwall and beyond. The poetry and stories here, written by both new and established writers, are inspired by this westernmost wilderness and its coastline, whilst also reaching outward to cities and places far from its shores in a rich map of fresh writing.

Told through five chapters: Journey, Body, Wings, Voice and Transformation, the core themes are maps, the sense of explorations, inner landscapes and journeys, body as map, borders, stopping points - and absence of them. You will be able to follow the path through the book as it explores land and place, then flesh, blood and trespass, before it soars with a shamanistic wing spread. Put your ear to listen as it speaks in tongues and finally settle to absorb its many tales. Or you can choose to dip and dive within its pages. Either way you will find treasures.

This is a cartography of women drawn with a myriad of tales – a reflection of the many contours of the landscape and the diversity of its people – with this book as a touchstone. The lines here are written upon, the blue of the sea, the stopping points, the scar, the words that were said, the horizon and the path ahead. Here we find snapshots of life in the developed Cornwall as well as its wild idyll, we look through a window to forced migration, land grab and diaspora. We revel in childhood, consider age, move through playful states and encounter the metaphysical, the surreal, the existential, the environmental, we bear testimony of violence and loss and we honour ancestry.

Linda Cleary

JOURNEY

I Knew Which Direction

from the way the moon tilted towards the sea. My heart,
pulled gently from my chest, was carried, sleepwalking
over the waves. I held my breath, concentrated
on the new space. There was pain, but it was not new pain.

Pray now, whispered the sand and I fell to my knees thinking:
moonlight, moonlight, moonlight —————
until it was no longer a word but a colour and then a feeling
and then the thing itself.

ALICE KAVOUNAS

Ornament Of Asia

What if, on a day in mid-September,
I awoke as usual to this idyllic view—
a crescent of a bay—but instead of Coverack
it's my father's city, Smyrna, nineteen twenty-two,
her harbour thick with battleships flying flags
from the world's so-called fair-minded countries.

Would I sense the danger on that brisk wind?
Would I try to leave? And if I panicked
what, besides the children, should I grab?
Would I abandon everything—even
the carefully tended fig, coming into fruit.
Would I be swayed by wild rumours . . .

mounted men are heading toward the city
set to sack and burn it . . . Or would I chance it
and stay, thinking, we've made our lives here
for thousands of years, trading in and out
of this city. *Flee? Flee to where? How?*
Look at the ships. They must be here to save us,
I would have thought. *Would I have thought that?*

And like as not, I might have rushed the children
through the stumbling crowds, fled from the 'safety'
of our house. I'd have joined the floods of people
edging toward the harbour, that numbed procession
with no exit plan, pushing for a place
on the last steamer, to get themselves out,
to go anywhere. Anywhere but here.

What if we plunged into the sea and swam
toward those smartly dressed crews—French, Italian,
British, American—on board, standing watch —
surely they'll see us coming! We're swimming
for our lives, stroking the water like it's the last thing
we will love . . . But wait—some crews are throwing back
the swimmers like small fish . . . we see them drowning,
drowning within inches of those foreign hulls.

We dog-paddle back to shore, breathless, trapped
between fire and the sea. The ships' masters declare neutrality.
Who would have us now, orphans of the 20th century:
Armenians . . . Jews . . . Ottoman Greeks . . . Palestinians . . .
exiled on the wrong side of history.

Note:
*In 1922, from the 11th-14th September, Smyrna was virtually
destroyed by fire. This was the culmination of the ongoing, brutal
conflict between the Anatolian Greeks and Kemal Attaturk's
victorious army. Strabo, writing in the Augustan age, described
Smyrna as the finest city in Asia, famous for its harbour, and as
Homer's birthplace. Known as the Ornament of Asia, Smyrna
rivalled ancient Ephesus.*

RUPAM BAONI

anonymous

yes, I dropped here from the land of
noise and monochrome, back there every-

thing was magnified to Hermon,
Wadi Hajar, al-Assad and the rest, I'm

anonymous; once we ate mud, ashes and
mortar, lived in houses baked to bronze and

char black, we carried pailfuls back and
forth from trenches spewing flame, gunge and

human blood; once I was swallowed whole
then regurgitated back to living again and things

moved on as before; once I was torn limb
for limb, head, torso, groins, then sewn back to

a piece, misshapen and make-do; once
evenings had the children hanging on by

a thread to tales of honey-baklava, *za'atar*, or
salvers of *kibbeh bil-saniyeh*, growing aches in

the underbelly, mounting shrieks outside of
our nights, the tears were gravel, the eyes stoned

upon the sea of no-return; once I was
born and killed in utero for I didn't know then

nor will, the secrets of birthing and of
death; yes, I am here now in my 206 or so

scraps and strips, my wedges of flesh, my skin,
my spleen, the three leftover faces that I call home

LAURA SENNEN

Full and Empty Spaces

A woman in a blazer looks up from a pad of paper and says, 'Have you thought about all the travel you'd need to do in this role? How would that be?'

'I've travelled in roles in the past. I know it can be a challenge, but I'm sure I can make it work.'

Looking back, she remembers how her mind strung thoughts together in this interview, thoughts like 'it doesn't pay to get too settled', thoughts like 'the time will pass more quickly if I keep moving around'.

...

My eyes close despite me and the world behind my eyelids is 170 years old. There's no sleeping or staying awake. Like a line's been drawn around me keeping me out of time, keeping me three or eight or twenty, keeping me quiet and half asleep. Hungry for the Wagon Wheel I know is hidden somewhere in my dad's pocket, as he closes off his face away from the world. I never think about what his life is like. I can sometimes catch a smell, of oil or something burning, that goes with the screeching of the wheels as we slow down round a bend. It will remind me of him.

There are empty spaces, and sometimes I can fill them with the swaying of the carriages and the jolts when they separate or join together. There are spaces that are full, like a moment after Easter when me and my sister were going home. We weren't supposed to say 'home' so we were just going back, away from the sea, to some station that this train track always seemed to take us to. Getting off the same carriage, stepping onto the same platform, walking down the same sloping twisted underpass with the same darkness round the edges, just never ending grey concrete. We knew where we were going, but not being able to say the word made us float into tangles in our heads and sometimes forget, or disappear. Any journey might end anywhere, might never end. Maybe we were already home, maybe we were never home. Maybe this journey was home.

And this day we united against the tangled disappearing and offered something to our journey, knowing it would be there for us. We could hear it at night whether we slept or not, could it hear continuing, always. Always the grey concrete waiting for our feet, always the biscuit hidden in a briefcase. Always the rules to remember, repeat, remember, pretending they made sense.

And we left our offering piled on a long seat in a First Class compartment; musty, dusty grey square-patterned seats, arms slotting into their spaces, we pushed them back and piled the eggs on top of one another, giggling for a minute, shocked for a minute, unbelieving at the thought of leaving these perfectly wrapped, shiny jewel coloured heavenly sweet smelling chocolate eggs, leaving them in their pile. To be found maybe by someone but we didn't think of that. It was enough to leave them balanced. To slide the glass door closed on them. To walk silently away, maybe glancing at each other once, before we reached out of the window and pushed open the door and stepped onto the waiting concrete.

...

There was a day when she looked at herself and saw something bright inside her right eye. She moved closer to the mirror, trying to look deep into the darkness of the pupil, because inside there, far back, she thought there was a map. Stylized and simplified, like you'd see on the wall of any station, behind a plastic sheet or sometimes behind glass. She couldn't get close enough to see the names of the stopping points.

VIVIENNE TREGENZA

Woman, cliff, islands

On the cliff edge
in a white-washed cottage
clinging to ancient rock
she felt years spread under her feet;
strata of muted colours
threaded here and there
with ribbons of gold.

She knew that she would live
precariously, weaving
her stories into song;
Tregeseal, Cape Cornwall, Lamorna
faded tapestries of childhood
made bright again.

Now the roof of the cottage
is ablaze with sunlight
and from a bedroom window
you would see the fog lifting,
a woman walking in the valley,
and beyond the sea's horizon
the delicate embroidery
of distant islands.

PENELOPE SHUTTLE

I Always Travel With A Map Or Two

Australia is the capital of Iran
France is a small provincial town in Finland
Costa Rica is clearly visible
in this aerial map of London
Estonia is the capitol of Bolivia
Barbados is very near the North Pole
I have maps drawn by clever men
to prove all this is true
Sunset goes up into the mountains
to seek her fortune
The moon is hiding in Russia,
the stars are visible only from Mexico
Madrid is on her knees
weeping for the old days
when she was Queen of Spain
long before
she became a homesick island
ten miles off the coast of Norway

Blood Borders

Straight lines ruled across the arid wilderness
divide up the spoils of empires,
regardless of cohesion, tribe or tradition.
These saber cuts, drawn for ownership, resources and power,
lay claim to the dessicated flesh of the great deserts
of Arabia, Syria and Sinai,
where ecstasy and death walk always together.
Fierce passion burns through the lens of maplines
in deep outrage at the desecration wrought by those long dead
mapmakers.
How, now, to read between the callused lines of conflict,
to cauterise the wounds of this careless rupture,
as violent as the Red Sea`s parting
yet wrought by very human agency?
How, but to kneel at the raw edge of the abyss,
in the deserts of the prophets,
and reach out a hand of wilful gentleness and trust
to the mirror beyond?

Perfume Map

My date sends me a map
made of perfumes,
curving paths of rose and clary-sage,
main roads of jasmine,
high notes of cathedral and slum,
ozone-rich as a city without cars,
the sanest gift ever.
I explore its fragrant zones
of musk and balsam,
byways of lemongrass,
a rainfall-on-moss avenue.
I turn a sandalwood corner,
cross a bergamot threshold,
meet him as easily as if I'd been born blind.

A View

I'll remember nothing from here, not this spider-webbed window, nor the view behind; not the concrete steps that divide my space from theirs, nor the opaque windows and empty roof-lights that illuminate the nights; the shapes that shift through the bars on the blinds. I will not remember the rain that stutters along iron pipes, that empties into the grid of leaves. I will not remember the invisible boom of waves or the crack of fireworks that echo around the stairwell, nor the seed-blown daisy that blooms and dries in micro-seasons on the white-washed wall, nor even the single star and seagull that sometimes punctuate this patch of western sky. I will forget all these.

I'm going east by the river, into Leonids meteor shower.

Although it is
November, I will sleep on the deck with a rope
and a bowl of water to capture the moon.

I'll float a bonfire of reeds
to carry the memories,
pipe   them
to the sea.

       sunrise will fall
         on my table

KATHERINE STANSFIELD

Bodmin Moor Time Capsule
under the gorse by the bridge

In a Quality Street tin
a sheep's skull. In the skull
my bike, my riding it. In my riding
granite, grazes from climbing it. In my grazes
a thorn tree, buckled. In the tree
a duckling in a striped cat's mouth; the duckling's

       down, gorse yellow. In the down
the flooded quarry, my fear of swimming

       and the swimmers. In my fear
such rage, raging to be heard. In my rage
the tors, their grey sternness. In their sternness
the sun, sometimes. In the sun
the sea, a shining wish a way away. In that wish
the wind, always the wind. In the wind
the bridge. In the bridge
the gorse. In the gorse
the tin. In the tin
so much fucking loneliness.

VIVIENNE TREGENZA

Sisters

Two girls on a granite bridge
above a twisting stream, dropped
crooked sticks. One snagged
in brambles, the other sank.

Tregeseal is hedged
with blackberries now.
Beyond No-Go-By
stands a disused mine.

KATRINA NAOMI

Elsewhere

When light prods
at the curtain   you look up
having been away
to a place where the news
did not exist
and the journey was calm
for these waters
                              Yet you
sense you've not travelled
enough   wish you'd tipped
over the horizon   known something
of the bend in the world

BODY

VICKI MORLEY

My Body Is A Boat

*I sailed on the river of time until capsized and beached. Here is
my frail old barque; cold, waterlogged and donated. It lies on the
porcelain altar under the unremitting stare of neon. There is a green
stink, lake slime, but the formaldehyde masks it. I view my corpse
with amusement, it served me well and now it will serve medics.*

'Today is cadaver day one. Before you are let loose, and you
will all have your own to cherish and cut, look at this one.
Think what you might find beneath the skin. Read a body as
a map. See what it might contain. Each one is unique and yet
they are all the same, a miracle. '

The student doctors gather round the first corpse. 'First
impressions, Mr Passmore?' He moves closer to the body, lifts
an arm, looks at the hands. 'Skin good, hair and nails poor, but
normal for a sixty-four year old woman and –.'

*No advantage to be female in the world of business, banking and
consultancy but the Civil Service lacked gender barriers. I had my
own staff. We all wore ID, worked as a team and never talked about
our work, outside the gates. That was forbidden. I was permitted to
buy executive vitamins from the internal shop. They weren't. Were
higher ranks supposed to keep their brains in better condition?*

*My division analysed radar communication along the western flank
of Russia. Using the scrambler phone to contact RAF and NATO
bases, it was a bonus to be female. Clear information was all that
was required. It didn't matter what you looked like; male, female, or
hermaphrodite, as long as you matched the photograph round your
neck.*

Mr Passmore shines a tiny torch around the mouth, counting

to himself. 'Teeth. They're interesting, Prof, some missing.'

*Mr Passmore is no slouch. The impacted wisdom tooth in the middle
of my first teaching practice is a torment. After a long hot day in
a glass-walled classroom, infants buzzing between the maths table
and the reading area, I'm ready to use my flit gun of sarcasm. But I
realise the tinies are hot, tired and sleepy. I gather them on the story
mat that smells of stale pee and biscuits, and read an adventure of
Paddington Bear, using different voices. They like that.*

*The school day is far too long for such small people, it seems endless
to me. After a week of painful hamster face, the dentist levers out the
offending tooth, and forty infants became manageable. They call me
Mum by mistake and one calls me Dad. Does his Dad wear a yellow
gingham frock?*

*No infant realises I also teach swimming. They've never seen me
in bathing hat and costume; I'm just another Miss, this time, an
aquatic one. I puzzle why items of clothing; pants, sock, or vest, are
abandoned in the changing rooms. A few infant flounderers can't
remember where they live, never mind which clothes are theirs. They
can't fasten buttons or put a shoe on the appropriate foot.*

*I switch to secondary. These monsters are fun; cheeky, knowing and
innocent about life, like infants without peach fuzz skin and button
mushroom noses. The same temper tantrums, but the blessed relief
of real conversation. They can write, take themselves to the toilet and
understand the task, even if they laze away the hour.*

'Mr Collings, take over.' He turns the leg around. 'Some scar
tissue here, Prof.' He points to a strange section of skin on the
left leg, just below the knee.

*My old corpse will be carved up and examined, cut again and again,
until the last offerings fit into a shoe box to be buried with speed.*

*That scar. I'm a bank clerk. The only female clerk in the branch to
apply for the banking exams; I'm considered odd. Law and economics,*

I pass. I find book-keeping dull. I fail but it's overlooked as I have an O' level maths.

Cheltenham Gold Cup night, the cashiers busy counting suitcases of cash, the bookies and the chief cashier smoking and joking. The smell of Rhodesian tobacco mingles with the beery stench of bookies' suits. Silver and copper coins clink on the scales, before dispatch to the vaults. I collect the remittances for day book, from their wire baskets behind each cashier.

I reach out to collect the final batch. My left leg disappears. My stomach lurches. I fall. Panic bubbles up. Pain, blood, shock Someone forgot to close the silver chute. I gain a scar that never tans.

'What is this?' The professor points to a tiny mark below the navel.

'Is it an appendectomy scar perhaps, Professor Whitaker, sir?'

'What! Look, it's too high for that. No, no, it looks like an investigative site. Perhaps for a small camera. What does that indicate?'

He has found the evidence for a laparoscopy, for sterilisation. By the age of forty and several lovers later I was married to a new spouse. We knew the parenthood road was not for us. Afterwards I recall my hospital breakfast, an anaemic chicken sandwich, white bread, no crusts. I identified with that chicken, my tubes had been cut.

'We've seen the outside gentlemen. Time to look inside. Anatomy is the basis of medicine. Mr Passmore, I think we are ready to watch you make the first incision.'

Is my old body an anaemic chicken waiting to be jointed, money in the bank of the medical school or a teaching aid? It doesn't matter. We are all stardust.

'This knife is a good one to start. Move back, he needs more room. I suggest you go in through the abdominal wall, just here. We will see the evidence of this woman's life for ourselves. Stop if you feel any nausea. Remember this body was donated to help you become a doctor, that's why we do this.'

PENELOPE SHUTTLE

For My Own Back

Shall it be sweet gum or birch this time?
Ash cane or hedgerow switch?
I choose the willow, wayward and unruly,
peeling the withy to a fierce thin rod
whose strokes across my naked back
brand a star chart on to my scarred pelt,
map for my own true lover to navigate by night.

Cold Fish

The October tides are greedy mouths at the shoreline. Bites of old concrete are sucked down with dead trees and drowned birds. Swathes of sandy beach migrate from one place without warning, only to appear the next day in another. A puzzle of smooth boulders remapping the coastline. Only the petrified edges of ancient forest and the crooked arm of the harbour remain constant.

Nobody notices as she navigates her way into the rising sea. Impatient clouds stand-by bulging at the seams, grimly urging her on. She moves further down the slope as a dark swell pours up around the corners of the slipway, slapping her thighs as she pushes deeper into the freezing water. Her legs go numb as air is forced out of her mouth in short whale blows.

As she launches herself further the diesel-green water covers her face. The taste of engine runs through her mouth like bad medicine as she forces her head underneath its oily surface. The cold feels insane; shards of pain pull at her scalp, biting into her face, burning her skin. Salt pours into her.

When she resurfaces exposed to the wind-chill, tiny steel blades chop at the bare bones of her neck, her hands claw-up in rheumatic spasm and her core muscles tighten. Just breathing is out of her control now, sharp and rapid. For a moment she wonders if she is going to die. It's just the cold shock response she tells herself, allowing the normal reaction to happen. Breathing slower, anxiety dissipates, and a feeling of calm and seeps into her mind. Adrenaline fuels her muscles as her heart rhythm comes into balance. Heading out of the safety of the harbour, she swims into the open sea towards the orange and blue marker buoys, a sense of power gives her a little rush.

Losing herself she thinks about an article on extreme swimmers. The sturdy heft of the highland women in their tea-cosy hats. They howl like banshees as they dive into dark lochs, their frozen hair, like tribal-warriors. She imagines herself as a fine-boned Norse woman breaking the ice to slip under the pure crystalline and listen to its songs, its cracking solidity. She feels jealous, envious of their extremes. Maybe one day she will go there, warm herself by birch fires, lie naked on ice beds. —Maybe stay there.

The clouds move out towards her, charting her return and she swims back towards the harbour. Suddenly she feels something, touch. Fear. A tangled thing around her arm. For a moment panic —a bloated acid-blue Portuguese man o' war, purple bursts of heart-spikes inside her ribs. She tries to shake free of the tendril, it brushes her face, she feels paralysed; electrocuted, as toxic pink lines track through her nervous system, injecting her with poison. It feels like a memory —the sting of grief.

Breathe! Breathing always saves her.

She laughs as she recognises the blue and red logo and rolls the strewn strips of plastic into a ball, sliding it under the strap of her costume. Her arms are tired as she fights to get through the waves breaking at the slippery-edged harbour steps. Losing her balance for a moment she is a toy at the mercy of crashing white waves, playing with her like massive cat paws. Gripping the pitted rusty rail next to the steps tightly, she rolls herself sideways, tiny peels of rust break into her hand and she beaches herself so as not to be dragged backwards across the sharp clusters of inky mussels. The rain finally starts to drop in goblet sized splashes. Proper rain. Wet rain.

As the season changes, the notches on the thermometer go down, long bad weather days are lost in a porous place. Dreaming of falling, slowly merging into the holding depths of steel-grey waters. Dreaming of being alone in an undersea world, a salted pathway. Reaching down into the kelp streams, the rivers of green and brown bubble skin, ripped trails of old paper, pointing her in directions. Long tongues wrapping around her like silk scarves. Ragged shellfish and welded limpets, their small alien mouths spurt strange liquid. Miniature jellyfish buzz as they pass by like electric flowers. The pulsing of tiny starfish as they curl their fingers around each other like babies do around a parent's thumb —The shape of them made her ache with something she had left on a shelf long ago.

A high tide brings seaweed up onto the beach paths, all over the place in heavy fishy lumps, waiting for something to dry it out and blow it back to where it came from. The edges picked at by sea birds. She piles it up in the bath, soaking in the green-brown juice of it. As the seaweed comes back to life under the running of the cold tap. It mesmerises her, turning, unfurling, growing, enfolding her like a river journey, transforming.

Her fingernails a bluish-grey, face sculpted, her skin almost green in the light of the open fridge door as she stands naked in the kitchen dripping wet. The sound of ice, dripping, dripping —dripping like sadness, dripping into sinks, pouring through windows, rushing into the gutters, flooding out to sea with the rain.

ABIGAIL ELIZABETH OTTLEY

The Gift

I bring you broken walls and sharks fin razor wire
grown into the hard lines of my stone-scape.

A handful of berries harder than a rosary
brighter than a maidens menstrual blood.

I bring you fallen leaves and a handful of petals
steeped in salt tears to make a potion.

Swallow it down. Its taste is quick and bitter.
Seasoned remedy of my ice-house years

I bring you bird song and the bones of small birds
green nuts that sleep on and dream of forests.

Blue-violet shadows, the mystery of roots
my spiked tongue, the snap of my spine.

DIANA DIXON

Still Life

Her limbs sat
in repose, resigned.

She is sitting in her chair,
both wheels aligned.

Waiting for the hands
consigned to move her.

RUPAM BAONI

dads, playoffs & sherry trifle

the widest distance between the thumb and
forefinger – that's how far removed I grow with

or without you now; it's all a matter of
puttying the odd crevice onto the strips of those

otherwise evenly painted walls I'm told, and we
could be family again; remember the warmness of

our summer afternoons, wet like the underside of a
tongue whose bloody pinks have blended to pale onyx

now? that's the span of time between child and
adulthood; and that's not enough anyhow to wipe out

those creases in a relation now suffixed with the
quintessential ship to it; yes, affixes never last; they

weren't meant to, nor were roots and root words; they
alter, reinvent themselves, slip to posterity; we weren't

meant to either; our love was sherry trifle and
crumble when it was and now it eats into us, starting

from head down to the far extremities; we'll never
shoulder it together to the final eulogies and back, just

as we never did to any back then when I'd waited up
there at the podiums, charged with anticipation and the

promise of many arrivals; yes, mum always did
say I was a trader of emotions, didn't she? she had hip

replacement last autumn after those ectomies; and she
said she loved the rustle of footsteps up the drive and that

her body reminded her of failure

ELLA FREARS

Hayle Services (grease impregnated)

His head in the front seat
is parboiled. I'm feeling
pretty empty packet, salty
foil. *No point in worrying
until we know* but oh hello
turmoil. Boots. Up-down
the aisles *do you have an oily
complexion*? Woman at the till
tries to get my eyes with hers.
Avoid! Toilet-bound, *do you
have an oily...* M&S escalator
groans, shudders, fan belt
of the universe turning.
Can't go! Foiled again, but then
OK anxious stream. Feel grimy,
a bit doomy. Pissy hands.
Whisper: et tu uterus? Replay -
recoil. The overwhelming
sense that I'm on trial, soiled,
ruined, spoiled. Mamma,
can you come pick me up?
30 seconds. Still wet and blank.
I'm in Hayle, oh not much really,
just waiting for the pink voila.

FAYE WILSON

I Am Becoming

I am becoming the hospital. My brain is the grainy black and white monitor showing me what I already know. The lack of pixels silently transmitting known news into my fibres.

My unconscious, unrelenting chicken scratch anxiety is the scarred, dirty skirting of the endless corridors. We are scraped raw with the abuse of innumerable knocks and weeping, exposing decades of old layers of protection.

The silent poison ceiling tiles and the violent buzzing fluorescent strip lights are my burned out optic nerves. Unwanted images have scalded white on to my retinas. There are things that I didn't want to see. There are things that the ceiling tiles want to forget.

My bones are the smooth pale frame of the hospital bed. Utilitarian and practical but inevitably weakened and altered by the often-remembered weight of so many souls passing through.

My throat is the tightening, enfolding bedding. Words are mostly stifling prickly blankets too big to cough up but the ones that do escape are crisp and white starched bed sheets. The sharp angles of the hospital corners are hard to swallow.

The cocooning curtains with their mocking and grotesque florals are my womb. The suns rays are able to penetrate their weave but they are unable to contain the glow for long. Delicate lilacs are the translucency of my babies' eyelids. A faded bluebell is the sorrow of unopened eyes. Pale buds are small fists that will never unfurl. Wispy reaching tendrils unseen in heavy folds will never know my touch or warmth.

The quiet air in the cubical is crying. It is tired. It cannot hold itself up any longer. It cannot be what it needs to be. It cannot keep anything alive.

Below, the worn-out linoleum is my life now. Every fleck is a piece of me. My babies. My heart. My courage. My grief. My marriage. My amaranthine hope.

DIANA DIXON

Sensing Her Fate

She didn't see
the figure's
shadow.

She heard
the slither
of his zip.

She felt his
body slam
into hers.

She tasted
her blood,
his hate.

She smelt
her fear,
his exit.

LUCIA OLGA GOMEZ JOHNS

Only Today

Only today
Only today I could ask why?
Only today I could say No
Only today I could put THE limit
THE boundary
After all those years
After all that fear
And confusion
It was blur
It was scary
It was and it wasn't
Almost reached
Out of reach
But today I'm facing it
I'm looking at it
I can really say
And I will say STOP
Not any more

PASCALE PETIT

Father's Maps

The only maps I want now
are in my father's chest.

I'll unpick the old scar,
part the sawn ribs,

spread his lungs out flat
on the airport runway –

all fourteen thousand square feet
of air cells.

ABIGAIL ELIZABETH OTTLEY

Confessions Of A Circus Performer

Poise is all — even when sleeping —
there is memory in musculature.

From girlhood onwards nights without ceasing
I have fine-tuned my entrances.

Ascending the ladder, every step a gamble
feeling the spring in the platform.

When I strike my pose I hear you whisper
Only remember to breathe.

To step into space is the hardest thing
feeling for the slack in the wire.

The sea-bed below me swims nightly with flatfish
their dim eyes turned up to see stars.

Now I am grown into the pink suit of my skin
my left toe extends to direct me.

Performance is all. That is the lesson
you have taught. Look. See how I fly.

WINGS

PASCALE PETIT

My Amazonian Birth

The arrival of colour – plumes of it piercing your lungs
as you take a first breath,

your eyes like thistles of light
that whirl,
        wondering
where shall we root?

Now, sunrays are the wings
of macaws,
        more sound than colour –
the cry that comes out of you is their tails
        flaring across a creek at sunrise.

*

You are dragged from the grove where colours
fly in faithful couples

as your Amazon mama is wheeled away –
her hair a coral tree against institution green.

The rainforest that engulfed you
is pushed away by orderlies,

            as if you're on a boat
            and the riparian walls glide past,

but it's the jungle sliding downstream,

not the boat
fighting the current as it noses the Puna foothills, towards your
    source.

Everything you need
is carried off on a gurney
to be packed in ice.

Your mama's face is a mudslide
as the septicaemia bites.

*

And your face, moving over the waters?

Your face that was once a rag of rain, slivers of you rearranged
        nightly in her womb,
the splinters sloshing like quicksilver as her fever spikes.

Your face that once was lodged in the mother-tree
        among branch-tributaries and fountains of palms.

Your face where the macaws nested
and the harpy eaglet hatched,

where the sloth crawled across your lips like a tongue on its
    first outing.

One eye is life the other death –
        two armadillos in their burrows.

One cheek is dawn the other dusk –
O the harmonies they sing! In the twilight
of your face-stem, the hum of the singing flower

no one has discovered!
Your mouth where vowels hover like bees!

*

One hand is day the other night.

The feet unfurling like epiphytes,
one shy one brave,
one with a treefrog between its toes, one with a cockroach,
but oh how the roach's armour shines with rubies and garnets!

And the toes that strangers will stroke as if to remember
    swinging through the canopy.
The soles that have not yet walked on concrete
but wriggle to follow an ocelot's trail,

curious for the bounty and the horror, wanting to watch the
    puma
crack a deer's neck in the hospital car-park.

*

Grief squatting in your heart
like a strangler fig high in a branch-fork,
                        that sends roots
down your chest and weaves a cage
around each hope –

your chest that, even as it's learning to breathe, feels vines
    tighten.

*

Your jungle-mama floating downstream now
until she reaches a firedoor
swung open then slammed, echoing down the corridor.

What a wind ruffles your caul,
for the river-silt still clings to you
and the uranus moths suck your salts.

A soaring in your head
that's a breakage
as someone wipes off the scat,

      your expression is
           now a flock of disturbed parrots
           now an egg that will not hatch.

A scorpion coils in the theatre lamp,
its sting poised.

*

Your bud-ears
hear the crash
as she reaches ICU
           so laden with orchids
           she topples to the floor.

There she lies, her roots upended like jangled nerves
they'll diagnose as anxiety
that slides into psychosis.

Butterflies jink over her trunk
even as her flesh rots
           and blossoms with fungi –

your broken mama
laid out like a long-table
                    for the rest of your life to feast on.

VOICE

LOU SARABADZIC

Fool Me Twice

Would you trust me
if I told you things in one language, then another?

Est-ce que vous me feriez confiance,
si je vous disais des choses dans une langue, puis dans une
autre?

Or would you think I'm playing you
if you weren't able to understand every single word?

Ou est-ce que vous penseriez que je me joue de vous
si vous ne pouviez pas comprendre chacun des mots que je
prononce?

Tell me, would you trust me?
And if not, why is that?

Dites-moi, me feriez-vous confiance?
Et si ça n'est pas le cas, pourquoi?

Is it because *traddutore, traditore*?
And your mum told you never to trust a translator?

Est-ce parce que *traddutore, traditore*?
Et que votre maman vous a dit de ne jamais faire confiance à
un traducteur?

Translator, traitor, truancy's treasure.
Should we at least share it?

Traduire, c'est trahir. Le trésor du truand.
Si on le partageait, au moins?
Would you trust me enough
to sit down here, holding an empty box?

Est-ce que vous me feriez suffisamment confiance,
pour vous asseoir ici, à tenir une boîte vide?

Look at my words.
Do you trust them?
do I
trust you enough
to let them go?
And when will I
finally trust
myself?

Hieroglyph Moth

When the white ermine wings
opened at night

like a book of frost
      smoking in the dark,

I understood the colours of vowels
painted on moth fur –

the black, red, saffron signs
of a new language.

Antennae grew from my forehead,
my tongue was restless in its chrysalis.

I felt lift-off
      as if my bones had melted.
I stepped out into the snow –

not even an exoskeleton to protect me
in this strange country.

KATHERINE STANSFIELD

Cornish / Welsh / space

I crossed the river to come to Wales
and found new friends with old friends' faces

> *avon*
> *afon*

that made for me a bridge of sound
to those old friends I'd left behind

> *pons*
> *pont*

across the river where I had lived
where place was all those friends had seemed

> *eglos*
> *eglwys*

until I heard my new friends' tongue
and in it learned what had been mute

> *bardh*

bardd

across the river where I had lived:
a gift within a gift, a ghost

    rohow
     rhodd

that haunts my new friends' tongue and holds
its speaking close, and though the stones

    men
     maen

are not the same and neither are the birds
the sea's the sea both here and there

    mor
     môr

and I have found inside them, home,
inside these sounds, inside them: home.

LOU SARABADZIC

Lewis Carroll's travel diary: the Jabberwocky through Russian, Dutch, German, Polish, and French

Wonderful and spread toasts
Or I am in vabe and alive:
All facial expressions were Borogi,
And my mother goes up and down.

"Carefully Dzeybbervok, my son!
Jaws biting, claws catching!
Beware of birds and avoid Yubzhub
Crazy Bandershnach!"

He took his sword in his hand;
He had been looking for someone for a long time,
So he rested on the Tumtum tree
And thoughtful.

And when he thought he was getting up,
Dzhabbervok through the eyes of a flame,
About the address of Tulgi,
And he was worried when he came!

A pair! A pair! And by
Lord Vorpal was choking!
He left him dead and turned his head
He went at a gallop.
"And you killed Jabberwock?
Hand in hand, my Balshniku!
Happy day!"
He was shouting with joy.

"TWAS Brillig" and easy
Or I am in vabe and alive:
All facial expressions were Borogi,
And my mother leaves.

Note:
With most sincere thanks to Google Translate

TRANSFORMATION

NATASHA CARTHEW

Distance Between All Things

Storm inside.

That's how it begins how they say it should be. How it feels to stand against the precipice, look out, fall back in. The boy with a mind set apart like a million undiscovered islands his heart a drifting boat barely able to keep afloat stands feet firm against the cliff edge and looks down at the ocean. He imagines the mackerel coming in on a good rising tide vast shoals chasing sand-eels beneath the warm cuddling cover of Cornish water.

Family business, men's work, but to a boy with all the soft corners and creases still in he could only think about the silken amber sand, the sound of other water whispered in the ear of a cowrie summer found shell.

He closes his eyes so the beacon of him doesn't give his whereabouts away, wonders how he got from there to here how he'd travelled all that way without Dad noticing; lip gloss, good shirt, neat nails, silly little things dressed up as nothing, honest. Mum was different, had an inkling as good as knowing, but down the years he had managed to catch her questioning eyes with a smile, sweet boy. It didn't matter now, the pleats had been flattened out the map pegged in his hair unravelling through his veins it swam with his thoughts, traced his skeleton, the blood of him.

The storm was not so rough that he couldn't pull Dad's boat into the surf not so fierce that he couldn't navigate find himself standing strong, a new person by morning.

Some kind of calm, a moment of silence, the hum of early sea birds and an undiscovered cave to step into, slip this skin. The fluidity of gender passing through like the seamless stream of nature, the shape of things to come if he thought it hard enough, soft enough.

His destiny etched into the palm-flesh of both hands, decipherable, the journey all bone ladders and sinewy swings some distant future perfectly balanced, but written in invisible ink, he knew this.

The distance between all things, first strides travelling at such speed to reach the end no matter the rocky stepping stones across foreign oceans and the borders that meant the difference between do and don't. He liked to trawl but loved to swim with the dolphins more, mermaid but greater than that, a life lived as a fish out of water, the community would take time to understand that, this.

The next step the cliff path, sinking sand, push the boat out, a promise to return before the time taken to look up, head for the horizon, the full moon rising, smiling, an exploration that had always lived inside, each contour every coordinate pointing toward daughter, sister, perhaps one day somebody's mother. The boy with the sea inside, breathing all the love he'd kept secret, in.

New chapter turned, a better cover to colour with all the palette of rainbow, the old map thrown and a better journey penned through, the route taken good enough to find true nature, the blank page and the storm inside as calm as the new day dawning, the sea-pinks rising, waving, a woman now.

LINDA CLEARY

Kill Your Darlings

He is running after a pigeon, his parasol fluttering behind him, his little legs unsteady yet wilful to the quest, towards the bird. The fountain is arching its waters to the sky and the river is lulling afternoon dreams. He is 5 years old and full of wonder.

I wish I'd had a grandmother who had told me stories of old and taught me how to love, but my grandmother was crazy, drunk and broken from too much pain.

Hush, little baby, don't say a word.
Papa's gonna buy you a mockingbird

The bird moves ahead of him, hopping, twitching its petrol coloured head side to side. He runs little steps, nearly trips, tries to clap but the parasol falls and as it sweeps down cutting across the sun the bird flaps its wings upwards and is gone.

I wish I'd had a mother who had took me in her arms and taught me how to love, but my mother was angry, hardened and broken from too much pain.

And if that mockingbird won't sing,
Papa's gonna buy you a diamond ring

He wanted me to meet him but I couldn't, I was too tired of it all, of the fire and the dying of the fire, and my body showed its sadness. I was standing near the fountain in Trafalgar Square, those great shots of water surging to my heart, those lions mute roar somehow still able to stir my passion but ever so slightly. It was fairly cold, but actually I cannot remember anything of the temperature, for I was consumed and yet absent. *Let it go*, I thought.

I'm meeting someone, I'm meeting my lover from many years ago, I'm meeting myself as I am now, the furious sound of the train. And I met you.

Strange, Time. And Love. Or what, was it something other? Something other than Love? I had held myself back, or not even had to, I just didn't feel anything significant. In fact it felt like a chore to go, a command I was following from the one who used to be my Master and now was weak in my mind. For others had replaced the pain so many times, I could no longer find my addiction to him. It was no longer itching below my skin. But yet, I went, and gradually over those hours I warmed and became coquettish once more, knew his desire and liked it, and I let him place those passionate caresses and kisses all over my body. He awoke me. But having awoken me, he disappeared. Again.

The bedside book. Hard silk. Hot ice cream. Memories of him.

Intimacy does not mean anything.

The excitement (rapture) of hide and seek

*

Circles of time, yet still the same place. The place is there, the place, the place is I wish I'd had a father who had sat me on his knee and taught me how to love, but my father was in another country, silent and broken from too much pain.

And if that diamond ring turns brass,
Papa's gonna buy you a looking glass

The family tree, roots that I have escaped from, branches that cannot hold me, and I - always I - having to search alone for the water to keep giving me Life.

The roots are the hands of my ancestors; rough with hard work, stretched with yearning, empty of children, clutching suitcases, wiping silent tears, burying the dead.

This tree is one I cannot climb, its arms will not hold me, it has no fruit. It offers no shade nor food.

Instead there is an empty space. Could be a cut out of my father, could be a cut out of my lovers, could be a cut out of my hopes.

And if that looking glass gets broke,
Papa's gonna buy you a billy goat

Eighteen years I waited from child to woman, waited for one letter to come.

I stared at the words, going over his lines in that one letter – the thoughts becoming engrained facts; heavy with ink

And on I waited, although I heard many words and was seduced by many with their eyes full of my light, and their words and poetry flooding my heart, yet like Psyche who at the moment of trust looks upon her lover so then they would leave. And my star heart would die again.

And if that billy goat won't pull,
Papa's gonna buy you a cart and bull

I see them between my legs, each one in that same place, it is like a madness, a psychotic audition, each one with his own style, some blend into one, some stand out. Dangerous angels.

*

One day you realise you don't know the exact date any more;
the date it began or ended. That date which before marched in
front of your head and gripped your heart tight - is lost. Just
as the memories of touch are gone. Though I can remember
your smile and your eyes. Thoughts of what happened come
in flashes, sometimes after months of respite – only yesterday
I tried to remember the last time you left the house, the final
closing of the door - and I couldn't hear a sound. I closed my
eyes to hear it; that angry shutting, that end; but the sound
wasn't there. And then I remembered that it hadn't happened
that way, with you. With you it was through the telephone
only and you said you wouldn't come again, that there was
nothing you needed to explain. For your heart had nothing to
forget.

And if that cart and bull turn over,
Papa's gonna buy you a dog named Rover

Now those men like ghosts, I watch their faces; perhaps I am
the ghost and what an advantage, those ravaged faces, time
held upon them, magic and flirtations no longer available in
their eyes – only age and the catching up of the body that has
eaten them.

And behind their ghosts are the priestesses of Babylon in the
temples of healing and the fish head priests, is the lapidarium,
the stones standing as a providence within the realm of
creation, epigraphs testify to the great importances now
replaced, the musty odor of the fall of the Romans, the air of
lovers now all gone, nations and empires now columns and
fragments, the gates to historic cities dissembled to tombstones
for their song, is the torn down theatre, citing fire hazard, some
of the beauty remains but much has become defaced, ugly,
built over, now one has to find charm in concrete. Some dirty

charm. Like a stolen fuck behind an abandoned building.

And if that dog named Rover won't bark
Papa's gonna buy you a horse and cart

Yet for him the tree was emanating light. It quivered and
moved, an archaic divine bird, a super conscious being;
sparkling, remembering, opening, responding, speaking,
awakening. Bright, white light. So much so, that it hurt
his eyes. He was looking for a way out of there, for a more
comfortable place within that forest for them both to lie down.
Perhaps there was a hut or covered area, for they were cold.
He was stumbling in the dark, trying to give out that he had
a plan, that everything was alright, that he could protect her
– keep her warm – that it was just the night and nothing more,
just some dark hours to wait through. And then as he trod
slowly over the dead bracken and tried in vain to find a resting
place there suddenly was the tree – somehow lit – alive with
light.

And if that horse and cart fall down,
You'll still be the sweetest little baby in town.

Do you remember when we experienced the tide turn, that
very moment, that magical flip of the water's pull as it started
to recede – just as we had begun to be oceaned yet still danced
with our veils to our mistress' song. It was you and I and the
great blue sea, it was you and I and an alchemical spell that
formed a priestesses' alliance in our hearts. Do you remember
when we felt that joy, sister, of embracing the path of the heart.

Memory, is like another land with no bridge. Only water that
is too strong and too wide to traverse.

The absence of everything kills me.

LESLEY HALE

Porthkidney Dune

The sand had shifted.
By the time I found the place
you were hardly there.

MARY CHARNLEY

Seen From An Artist's Window

Sarah glances at the leaflet.

*'The artist has created a new moving image work using film taken
from the window of his beach studio. His study of figures in a littoral
landscape is distanced by the physical remove of the camera view
through a window.'*

Well at least its dry in here. She checks her lipstick and fluffs
her hair. Endless Cornish drizzle does it no favours.

A man approaches them, the gallery owner, maybe, a leftover
leftie from the sixties with his greasy grey hair and his faded
jeans. He flicks a switch and images move across the walls.
What is this supposed to be. A cinema or an art gallery?
Conceptual, abstract, representational? Denis tried to explain
it all to her once, condescending, The new Denis: accountant to
aesthete in barely six months.

Curious, she moves closer. Just a film? A beach. People are
moving across the screen doing nothing very much as far as
she can see. Denis is deep in conversation with the gallery
owner, flushed and reverential.

'Distanced from our gaze windows, identities once removed.'

He leans forward placing one finger against his top lip, feeling
the importance of holding his gaze, wondering how he looks
looking. She finds it easier to laugh at him than to love him
these days.

Figures move backwards and forward on the screen, caught in infinity. She waits for some action and then spots a young man sauntering along the beach, his surfboard like a monstrous phallus tucked under one arm. She looks at the leaflet again.

'From his window, the artist painstakingly constructs and deconstructs, re-collaging the images.'

The film is on a continuous loop. Is there a purpose to this? What is she meant to feel? The surfer passes by again and she wonders what it would be like to be young, to feel the power of the sea, the waves thrusting against you, re-discovering your youth.

An elderly couple amble across the screen. He helps her as she stumbles on the rocks, bends towards her and kisses her cheek. Such intimacy and love. Sarah sighs, and looks away. She hears the words; *'rhythmic behaviours, communal isolation'* and wonders for a moment what it would look like if she and Denis were walking on that beach, three feet apart and nothing to say. How would other people see them? A dispirited couple, the wrong side of fifty, disconnected and alone. That's what it's all about, she thinks in a rare moment of insight. Watching as if through a camera, slowly, recollecting, free from distraction.

She remembers a beach in Italy. Was it 30 years ago? She and Denis on honeymoon, walking in the moonlight, feet bare, the white sand between her toes. the evening breeze warm against her bare shoulders, his arm around her. Happy just to be.

Denis is talking now, eager and intelligent. 'Well, yes, the movement of the ocean, a fabulous beast, how it turns direction, forever changing, different identities.'

Were we so different in those days? Perhaps we were too

young and didn't know the people we would become. Have we grown and changed, each stage separating us more and more? Sarah's eyes follow the sea, constantly changing and then rearranging itself like the characters on the screen, moving backwards and forwards. The man with the faded jeans is talking again. Denis listens, nodding slowly, hand on hip.

'Yes, the sense of the body as a vehicle, the constant search for one's real self. See how their identities are revealed in a new light, the prism of the artist's gaze revealed in the ever changing sea.'

Different identities? Yes of course, that's all of us. but how often do we really see? With our emotions as well as our eyes?

Another scene. A girl suns herself on the beach, reminding Sarah of that holiday in Benidorm: young, single, lying there in her new bikini, full of anticipation. What changes she wonders? People say it's all down to your hormones, the menopause, but she thinks it's something to do with running out of joy.

She met Denis on that holiday.

New images drift across the landscape in a continuous loop. Sarah sees a woman in the top left hand corner framed by the mullioned window. Drooping shoulders, a twist to the mouth, a universal middle-agedness. A woman who believes that if life had treated her differently… The sea pounces, giving and taking away, never satisfied.

That could be me she thinks.

She sees a young couple, followed by two small children and

remembers another beach holiday. Six years old, sandcastles and sandwiches gritty with sand. Her father with his rolled -up trousers, her mother thin and silent in her deckchair as if waiting for someone to colour her in. She ran off to the sea when they weren't looking. Oh, the thrill of it, the chill of it, the sense of power, but there was always a price to pay for breaking the rules.

'Sensible shoes', that's how she would describe her childhood. It stays with you doesn't it? That fear of trying something new, of getting it wrong.

Images twice removed, the lens of the camera, the glass of the artist's window, herself a shadow, the woman she might have been. She thinks of the elderly couple, their painful progress across the rocks, and sees herself and Denis, twenty years on.

Where will we be then? We could run that film backwards couldn't we, start all over again?

The surfer re-appears as the sea nosedives, white foam leaping, and she longs to crest that wave, to feel that exhilaration as it throws her against the shore. It's not too late is it?

Denis walks towards her, paunch spreading over salmon pink chinos. 'What do you think darling?' he says. 'Isn't it wonderful? So thought provoking.'

Sarah smiles, beginning to understand.

ABIGAIL ELIZABETH OTTLEY

Tilbury Marshes, 1959

Girl-child playing on the whistling foreshore
mud squeezing worms between bare blue toes

long hair flashing the colour of new pennies
unfurling like a pennant

eyes shooting sparks as she digs and digs
locked in combat with the mud that
frustrates her

over and over filling her bucket
heaving it onto its rim.

Flushed and breathless she sits on her heels
sees another sloppy castle topple over.

Too much grey water grey marshes, grey sky.
This is no proper place to build.

JACKY GARRATT

The Derailment

The journey started in the last place you'd expect a journey to start: at a dead end. The perfect place to set out… in a completely different direction.

Backtrack: I was poring over my notebook.

"You're just a dog-end being ground under somebody's heel. That's education. And it goes on and on, until they're sure your light is well and truly out…"

But sometimes, I thought, people just chuck dog-ends out of car windows, don't they? They roll down the road, and the wind catches them, and they burn brighter and brighter, till suddenly they're at Doncaster and they've hopped onto a train and the next thing you know there's THE SOUTH and someone's saying…

ALL CHANGE PLEASE, ALL CHANGE!

Stillness penetrates my concentration. The train's stopped. I should be getting off. But the door's stuck. Hell's teeth, open up!

The train check's already done. The guy's gone. He's missed you. Everybody's gone.

I hear the engine shunting away, and that's it. I've literally been sidelined.

Well, you raged for a long time didn't you? Kicking the doors, ranting, crying, shouting "Let me out! I'm like a caged animal in here!" And from somewhere that Buddhist wanker said, "To tame a wild horse, you need a big field." And you thought, "Oh fuck off will you! You can take your half-baked philosophy and... Oh never mind... I'm out of here..."

But there's nowhere to go. I'm in the sidings, I'm locked in and I'm all alone.

Weren't you listening? The man said ALL CHANGE PLEASE! That didn't exclude you.

But I don't know how to get out.

Exactly. You've misunderstood. He didn't mean change trains, he meant CHANGE.

Tough isn't it? Sorry. There is no asterisk by your name and a paragraph at the bottom of the page in very small writing saying THIS ONE is hereby formally exonerated from all suffering, and can remain in perfect health and happiness, doing exactly what she fancies, all the time, forever and ever, without consequence, amen.

No. Nobody ever actually said that.

This is your opportunity, your golden ticket, except... it's for a train that doesn't move.

Golden ticket? Don't talk soft! I'm stranded. What kind of opportunity is that?

I know, I know. Its called sitting with it. It's horrible isn't it? IT is what the train has been running on all your life: anguish, agitation, pain. That compulsive drive to keep moving. Drink, eat, fuck... anything but THIS. This IMMOBILITY.
Yes, I need to GO!

Where have you been trying to get to? I did try to be gentle, but you wouldn't listen. A spanner in the works is all I could do in the end. The train ride's over for now. Normal service WILL be resumed as soon as possible. But that depends on how quickly you cotton on.

All the places you've been... yes, you chose the track. But I'm the fire in your engine. Without me, you're nothing. Bit of a fall, eh? You're not as smart as you thought. Pride comes and all that. If you DO get going again though, you don't need to exhaust yourself, running alongside the train, trying to hurry it along like you used to. Or even more hilarious, trying to push it sideways to make it change direction. You can just sit and start behaving like a passenger. All the sights, sounds, smells, well… you can appreciate them.

But get this. Life ISN'T a journey. You've already arrived. Start point, destination... they're the same. Being in the carriage. That's it. This is your Little Gidding moment. That annoyingly obtuse poem - you've finally cracked it. All the horrible bits of yourself you've tried to pretend aren't in the carriage with you, well... they are. You'll get to know them for the first time. But don't worry. They're just monsters under the bed. There was never really anything dangerous there. Just a trick of the light you might say. Or the absence of it.

Please remember: none of your belongings can be taken with you when you leave the train.

Look. I'm confused. Are you an announcement? Or am I going potty? Arguing with my*self*? I don't know whose voice is whose. Are you me, or someone else?

No one replied. I tried hard not to sleep. I was frightened. But I must've slept, because I woke up. And when I woke, the roof of the carriage was no longer there, just drizzling open sky. My first thought was escape, but I couldn't get any purchase on the plastic coated walls. So I just sat there, sweating into the prickly upholstery.

Full sun on my face came and went, afternoon cloud gave me respite. I spent hours, years maybe, amusing myself looking at the fabric on the seats with my eyes out of focus, seeing what I could see in the pattern. Evening fell. I dreamed of rain.

When I woke again, the walls were just a jagged remnant. I could have stepped over them, but now the carriage was reeling on a muddy torrent, so getting out was no longer a good idea. At least the rocking was soothing. In fact it made it hard to keep awake.

A slap of brown water in the face yanked me out of another dream. The carriage had sunk. I panicked and started thrashing around, but as I tired, I had to think more rationally. There was nowhere to go. The best strategy was to lie back and let the flow support me - for as long as I survived. If I drowned, I drowned.

But I didn't.

Stranger things began to happen. I lifted my dripping arm out of the water to find half of it was no longer there. I was disappearing. It was quite painless. Even when there was nothing of me left, physically I felt the same as I always had. Emotionally, bizarrely, I was perfectly happy. In fact, imperturbable. Nothing would unsettle me ever again.

MARY J. OLIVER

Warm Rain

When I was five or six, it dawned on me
that (like the sparrow the cat brought in
and Jesus on his cross) my parents would
one day die, the thought so hideous it
silenced me for a week, which drove them
to distraction but I didn't know how to explain.

After they died, my perverse imagination
dangled before me an image of my
daughter's wraithe. My child. Old. Pale as
a bone. Struggling to breathe. Calling out
to me. I wasn't there. Then warm rain
poured down from a cloudless sky onto her face.

WRITER BIOGRAPHIES

Ella Frears is a poet originally from Cornwall now based in London. Her debut collection *Shine, Darling* (Offord Road Books 2020) was a Poetry Book Society recommendation and is shortlisted for the Forward Prize for Best First Collection. Her poems about the St Ives' Modernists are currently on show at Tate St Ives.

Alice Kavounas lives on Cornwall's Lizard Peninsula. Born in Manhattan to Greek parents who left Europe for America, she read English Literature at Vassar. Her poems and short stories have appeared in London Magazine, Granta, TLS, Poetry Review, on BBC, and in Faber's anthology *Out of Fashion*, edited by Carol Ann Duffy. *Abandoned Gardens Selected & New Poems* is her third Shearsman publication. Alice and developer John Kennedy created the Poetry-in-Place app Words in Air.

Rupam Baoni is a critically acclaimed writer and artist. Her poems, short stories and articles appear in journals and newspapers. Her book of poems *Green, Red & Amber* received literary accolades and she has been longlisted for both the Commonwealth Prize and the National Poetry Competition. She has a new collection of poems being released shortly and she is currently writing a first novel as well as working on paintings and sculptures for solo exhibitions in Europe. In 2009 she was Writer in Residence at the Hypatia Trust and she distributes her time between St Ives and London.
www.rupambaoni.com

Laura Sennen works as a psychotherapist and lives in Penzance, Cornwall. In her writing and other work she is interested in the different ways people experience and occupy space, interpersonally, geographically and politically. This is her first time to be published.

Vivienne Tregenza is a Cornish poet. A former teacher (BA French & English Durham, PGCE Exeter) she returned to a childhood love of poetry in 2007. Short-listed for the Bridport Prize; Formal Prize winner, 'Poetry on the Lake' Orta, Italy (2008); she continues to be successful in international competitions. Well published in poetry journals and anthologies, Vivienne is completing her first collection and editing pamphlets for publication as well as volunteering and reading poetry in the local community.

Penelope Shuttle has lived in Falmouth since 1970, and is widely published. Her full-length collection *Lyonesse* will appear from Bloodaxe Books in 2021. *Encounters on a Bench*, her radio poem set in Falmouth, was broadcast on BBC Radio 4 in March 2020. *Will You Walk A Little Faster?* was published by Bloodaxe Books, 2017. She is currently working on a new collection, *History of The Child*.

Jude Brickhill lives in Gweek on the Lizard. Before beginning her writing career, she sailed around the world with her young family for several years in a traditional Cornish lugger, keeping the log, publishing travel articles and gathering grist for her writing mill. On her return to Cornwall she worked for many years as a yachting journalist, sailing and reviewing the latest small boat designs. She still sails but now writes mainly poetry and short stories. This is her first published piece of fiction.

Lesley Hale is a UK northerner who came to live in St Ives twenty years ago. She spends her time walking and swimming, working with local community projects, sometimes writing and performing. Her work has been published in journals and anthologies in the UK and USA, most recently in the Atlanta Review (Spring 2020) and a podcast from Alternative Stories.

Katherine Stansfield grew up in the village of St Breward on Bodmin Moor and now lives in Cardiff. She has published two full length poetry collections and a pamphlet with Seren.

Katherine is also a novelist: her historical crime series *Cornish Mysteries* has won the Holyer an Gof Fiction Prize and been shortlisted for the Winston Graham Memorial Prize. She co-writes a fantasy crime trilogy with her partner David Towsey, publishing as D. K. Fields.

Katrina Naomi received an Authors' Foundation award from the Society of Authors for her third collection, *Wild Persistence,* (Seren, 2020). Her poetry has appeared on Radio 4's Front Row and Poetry Please, and on Poems on the Underground. Katrina was the first poet-in-residence at the Bront Parsonage Museum and was highly commended in the 2017 Forward Prize for Poetry. She has a PhD in Creative Writing (Goldsmiths) and lives in Penzance. www.katrinanaomi.co.uk

Vicki Morley lives in Penzance and writes mainly poetry but also short stories. She was placed 1st in The Plough by Philip Gross 2016, Highly Commended by Sarah Howe Winchester 2017, published in WoLF anthology 2018, South 2019, short-listed in the last nine at Canterbury Poet of the Year 2019 and published in Ink Sweat and Tears, The Beach Hut and Atlanta Review in 2020.

Benigale Richards is a writer, performer and facilitator. She has recently completed an MA in Creative Writing at Plymouth University. After travelling widely and living in France and Spain, she returned to Cornwall and lives in Penzance with her daughter.

Abigail Elizabeth Ottley's poetry and short fiction has appeared in two hundred outlets including, most recently, The Lake, The Atlanta Review, Blue Nib, Impspired and Fragmented Voices. She won the One Million Story Challenge in 2011 and, in 2019, a selection of her poems were translated into Romanian for Pro Saeculum. Abigail is a former English teacher with a lifelong interest in history. She is also carer to her very elderly mother. (Abigail Elizabeth Rowland writes poetry and short fiction publishing as Abigail Elizabeth Ottley)

Diana Dixon has developed a new mantra: 'Observe like a journalist, write like a poet.' Her work has featured in several anthologies and women's magazines. She lives and works as a sculptor in Newlyn, where she 'writes in her head whilst sculpting with her hands'.

Faye Wilson is a Cornish born jewellery maker and reiki practitioner. She studied Graphic Art and Illustration at Anglia Polytechnic in Cambridge and has always been interested in exploring her creativity. She began writing flash fiction in 2017. Themes of folk law, magical realism, womanhood and empowerment have always been woven through both her written work and jewellery. This is her first time to be published. www.stuffmadefromthings.com

Lucia Olga Gomez Johns was born and grew up in Colombia (South America), studied Psychology and specialised in Environmental Education; subjects that allowed her to work with communities of different backgrounds, motivating people to take active part in environmental projects that could affect positive change in their lives. She has worked as a psychotherapist with individuals, couples and families; over in Colombia and now in Cornwall, where she moved nearly fifteen years ago. She lives with her husband and two children. This is her first time to be published.

Pascale Petit was born in Paris, grew up in France and Wales and lives in Cornwall. She is of French/Welsh/Indian heritage. Her eighth collection, *Tiger Girl,* published by Bloodaxe in 2020, won a Royal Society of Literature 'Literature Matters' award while in progress and a poem from the book won the Keats-Shelley Poetry Prize. Her seventh collection, *Mama Amazonica* (Bloodaxe, 2017), won the Royal Society of Literature's Ondaatje Prize 2018, was a Poetry Book Society Choice and was shortlisted for the Roehampton Poetry Prize. Four of Pascale's earlier collections were shortlisted for the T.S. Eliot Prize.

Lou Sarabadzic is a French bilingual writer and translator based in the UK. In 2019 she stayed in Charles Causley's house in Launceston for three months as a Writer in Residence, thanks to the Causley Trust and Literature Works. She writes poetry, fiction, and non-fiction, and won the 2017 DOT Award for Digital Literature. She delivers Creative Writing workshops to people of all ages. Read more about her work on her website: www.lousarabadzic.com

Natasha Carthew is a Working Class Country Writer from Cornwall. She has written two books of poetry, four acclaimed novels; *Winter Damage, The Light That Gets Lost* and *Only the Ocean* (Bloomsbury Books) *All Rivers Run Free* (Quercus) and her latest *Song for the Forgotten* (National Trust Books). Natasha writes extensively on the subject of Wild Writing and Working Class Fiction, including Writers' & Artists' Yearbook, The Bookseller, BookBrunch, Radio 3&4, The Guardian, The Big Issue and the Dark Mountain Project. Natasha is also the Artistic Director for the Festival for Working Class Writers, as part of the Festival of Ideas, 2021.

Linda Cleary lives in Penzance, Cornwall. She is a British born Irish heritage poet - writer performer from a northern English working class background and has travelled widely. She was Writer in Residence at Canserrat Art Residency, Barcelona and her work has been published across written and spoken word, audio and poetry film platforms including Poetry Bay, Long Islander, Citizen 32, Apples & Snakes, Berlin Zebra Poetry Film Festival and Poetry Film Live. She is Publishing Lead for Hypatia Publications, Director of her own company Free Writers Centre delivering Courses, Coaching and Editing service and has a preloved poetic clothing online shop Lit Wear www.freewriterscentre.org

Mary Charnley started writing following her retirement. Since then she has had several short stories published, has completed her first novel and gained an MA in Creative Writing from the University of Lancaster. She has a particular interest in writing for well being and in encouraging children to write creatively outside of a prescriptive school setting. She is now writing a second novel.

Jacky Garratt has had a range of jobs. Latterly, and for the longest spell, she was a doctor in the NHS, specialising in psychiatry. Ironically, medicine made her ill, so she had to give it up. She is now retired, and the many notebooks she has filled during her life are beginning to see the light of day. She has become a published songwriter and lyricist. This is her first published piece of fiction.

Mary J.Oliver lives in Newlyn, Cornwall. Her background is in the visual arts although she now focuses on writing. Her debut, *Jim Neat,* was published by Seren Books, October 2019. Her poems have appeared in anthologies in UK and US and in 2017 she was awarded 2nd prize by New Welsh Writing. She edits Piccolina, a newsletter promoting poetry in Cornwall, and runs workshops at the Hypatia Trust on cross-genre life writing. www.jimneat.com

ACKNOWLEDGEMENTS

I wish to give thanks to all the writers that have generously contributed their work to this book and to the publishers Bloodaxe, Seren and Offord Road Books for kindly releasing several of the pieces.

I have been blessed to have the mentoring of an experienced literary professional, Philippa Brewster, who has gone over her hours to advise and support me. I have learned so much under her guidance.

Thanks to Hypatia Trust, of which Hypatia Publications is an imprint. Amongst other aims Hypatia Trust supports and promotes women's cultural achievements and addresses gender inequality in their working lives. Special thanks to Dr Melissa Hardie, Founder & Director, for starting the original Hypatia Trust journey.

I want to salute Cultivator Cornwall and especially Sam Jackman who has been an absolute star in supporting this publication and the ongoing work Hypatia Publications is committed to.

And many thanks to you, dear reader, I hope that you do not just enjoy this anthology but that it also opens lines of enquiry and perception within you – as any good writing should.

*

The editor and Hypatia Publications would like to thank the following poets and publishers for permission to reproduce their work:

P8. I Knew Which Direction - Ella Frears, *Shine, Darling* (Offord Road Books 2020)

P20. Bodmin Moor Time Capsule under the gorse by the bridge - Katherine Stansfield, *We Could Be Anywhere By Now* (Seren, 2020)

P22. Elsewhere - Katrina Naomi, *Wild Persistence* (Seren, 2020)

P36. Hayle Services (grease impregnated) - Ella Frears, *Shine, Darling* (Offord Road Books 2020)

P41. Father's Maps - Pascale Petit, *The Zoo Father* (Seren, 2001)

P44. My Amazonian Birth - Pascale Petit, *Mama Amazonica* (Bloodaxe, 2017)

P52. Hieroglyph Moth - Pascale Petit, *The Treekeeper's Tale* (Seren, 2008)

P53. Cornish / Welsh / space - Katherine Stansfield, *We Could Be Anywhere By Now* (Seren, 2020)